PROM Praise

SOLOS

Volume One

Edited by
Noël Tredinnick

Marshall Pickering

Langham Arts : Jubilate

Marshall Morgan & Scott
Middlesex House, 34 42 Cleveland Street, London W1P 5FB

Copyright details will be found with each item. Every effort has been made to trace copyright holders and obtain permission; the publishers would welcome details of any error or omission, which will be corrected in future reprints.

First published in 1989 by Marshall Morgan & Scott Publications Ltd., part of the Marshall Pickering Holdings Group, a subsidiary of the Zondervan Corporation.

British Library Cataloguing in Publication Data
Prom Praise Solos : Volume One
  1. Songs, English
  I. Tredinnick, Noël

  ISBN 0-551-01920-4

Also from Marshall Pickering with Jubilate: *Let's Praise!* and *Carol Praise*.

Music and text set by Barnes Music Engraving Ltd., East Sussex.
Printed in Great Britain by Henry Ling Ltd., Dorset Press, Dorchester.

Prom Praise Solos
Volume One

Edited by Noël Tredinnick

Performance notes

Some items can also be sung by unison chorus or by alternating men's and women's voices.

Orchestral parts are available from Langham Arts, 2 All Souls Place, London W1N 3DB and, in addition to keyboard, the scoring is as follows:

I will praise you
      strings, 1 flute

Marriage at Sunrise
      strings, 2 fl, 2 ob, 2 cl, 2 fg, 2 hrn, 2 tpt, 3 trb, timps, perc, harp

Father, although I cannot see
      strings, 1 flute

Remind me, Lord
      strings, 1 flute, 2 horns

Jesus, how lovely you are
      not scored

Show me the way
      strings, 2 fl, 2 ob, 2 cl, 2 fg, 2 hrn, 2 tpt, perc

Better than I know myself
      strings, 2 fl, 2 ob, 2 cl, 2 fg, 2 hrn (plus rhythm section)

Behold the Man
      strings, 2 fl, 2 ob, 2 cl, 2 fg, 2 hrn, 2 tpt, 3 tbn, timps

Some of the songs in this collection have been recorded by the All Souls Orchestra conducted by Noël Tredinnick on:

Crown Him – Prom Praise at Wembley	Cassette	WSTC 9693
	Album	WSTR 9693
Prom Praise at the Royal Albert Hall	Cassette	LANG C 001
	Album	LANG R 001
	CD	LANG D 001
Hymns for Today's Church	Cassette	LANG C 002

Available from Langham Arts, 2 All Souls Place, London W1N 3DB.

Preface

Prom Praise has been presented for over ten years as a musical celebration of the Christian faith. It features a lively orchestral concert and much enthusiastic audience participation – just like the "Last Night of the Proms".

But an equally important ingredient is the vocal solo which has brought much blessing and encouragement to members of the audience. These solos have been performed by singers with some classical singing technique and with the ability to sustain long-running passages, phrases with high notes, accompanied by full orchestral arrangements. The range, vocal production and breath control required have made these songs apt vehicles of communication for suitably gifted singers. Within *Prom Praise*, many solos are accompanied by some kind of instrumental ensemble (if not full orchestra), and they vary in style. Some require the grand gesture, while others are meditative and soothing. The words and music have been sought after by others, and we are glad to be able to make them available at last. We hope that singers (male and female) with some measure of vocal technique will now enjoy performing these songs, whether in a church or concert hall.

This volume is a joint production between Langham Arts and Jubilate Hymns. I am particularly grateful for the tireless energy of the Jubilate team, and for the speed of Barnes Music Engraving, in processing this material for publication. In particular my thanks go to Catherine Fish, Bunty Grundy, Michael Mack Smith, David Peacock and Michael Perry.

I should like to dedicate this first collection with affection and thanks to Elisabeth Crocker, Kathleen McKellar Ferguson and Catherine Fish who in their turn first brought these compositions to life, so beautifully in *Prom Praise*.

Noël Tredinnick

I will praise you

From Psalm 9
Words and music: Nigel Swinford

I will praise you, O Lord, with my whole heart; I will show forth all

Marriage at Sunrise

Bridegroom Song

Words: Colin Day
Music: Nigel Swinford

see page 4

Father, although I cannot see

Morden

Words: John Eddison
Music: Norman Warren
arranged John Wyatt

Moderato

1 Father, although I can-not see the fu-ture you have planned, and though the path is some-times dark and hard to un-der-stand: yet give me faith, through joy and pain, to trace your lov-ing hand.

2 When I re-call that in the past your pro-mis-es have stood through each per-plex-ing cir-cum-stance and ev-ery chang-ing mood, I rest con-tent that all things work to-geth-er for my good.

 see page 4

3 What-ev - er, then, the fu - ture brings of good or seem - ing ill, _____ I ask for strength to fol - low you and grace _ to trust you still; _____ and I would look _ for no re - ward, ex - cept _ to do your will, _____ ex - cept _ to do your will.

Flute Solo

Moderato   Verse 1   Verses 2 and 3

ad lib. cadenza

suggestion:

Remind me, Lord

Words: Margaret Bowdler
Music: Norman Warren

Jesus, how lovely you are

Words and Music: Dave Bolton
arranged Noël Tredinnick

Chorus 4

Show me the way

Words and music: Wendy Craig
arranged Noël Tredinnick

Recorded by Catherine Fish on *Prom Praise at the Royal Albert Hall.*   see page 4

Words and music: © 1987 Eaton Music,
8 West Eaton Place, London SW1X 8LS

Better than I know myself

Words: from Psalm 139
Judy McKenzie
Music: Dave Cooke
arranged Noël Tredinnick

Verse

1 You were there at the mo-ment I be-gan, when the child be-came a
(2) here: so let it rain or let it shine, you are with me all the

man — saw my fu-ture in the mak-ing, saw the path my life was
time — when I'm wak-ing, when I'm sleep-ing, in the se-cret thoughts I'm

Recorded by Kathleen McKellar Ferguson on *Crown Him – Prom Praise at Wembley.* see page 4

* The accompaniment of the 'instrumental section'
can be inserted here for the repeat (10 bars).

8va bassa

Behold the Man

Words and music: Jimmy Owens
Music arranged Noël Tredinnick